Usborne

My First
Big Book
of
Doodling, Drawing
and
Colouring

Pictures drawn by
Josephine Thompson,
Caroline Day,
Vicky Arrowsmith
and Sam McPhilips

Words written
by Fiona Watt
and Anna Milbourne

Finish the fence...

Doodle more buildings ...

...and add some more trees.

...and draw more cars.

splash!

Draw penguins on the ice and swimming in the sea.

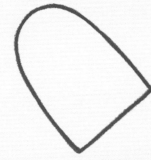

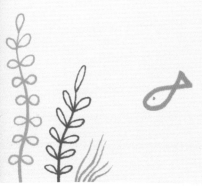

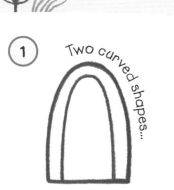

(1) Two curved shapes...

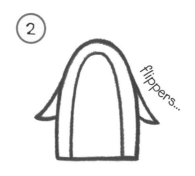

(2) flippers...

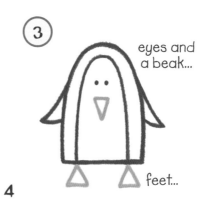

(3) eyes and a beak...

feet...

(4) and fill it in.

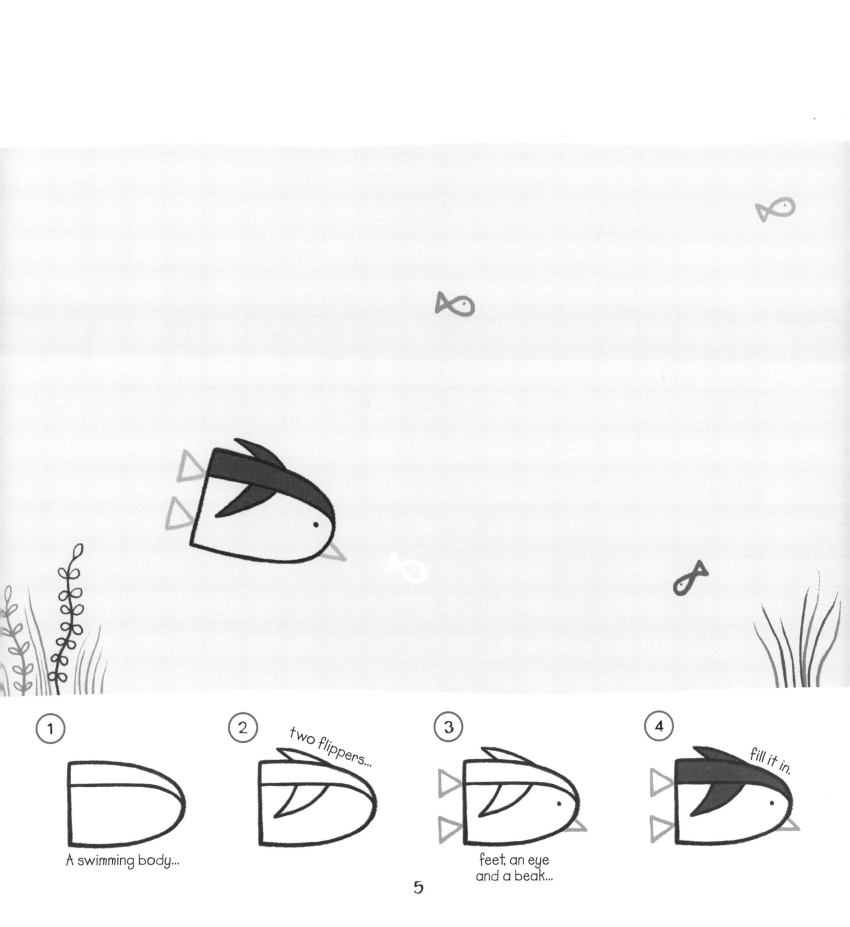

1 A swimming body...

2 two flippers...

3 feet, an eye and a beak...

4 fill it in.

5

BEEP!
BEEP!

Please complete us.

Whirr...
whirr...

7

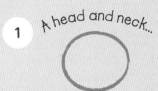

1 A head and neck...

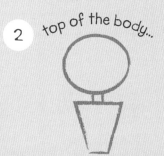

2 top of the body...

3

a big skirt...

add hair...

4

Draw princesses in a palace garden.

8

5 sleeves and arms...

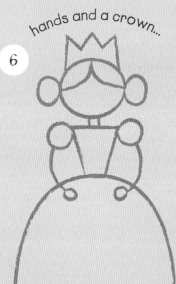

hands and a crown...

6

eyes and a smile.

7

9

Doodle stripes for tigers, curly manes for lions...

...or spots for a leopard.

Roar!

If you make each boat look different
you can tell which one is which
from way across the sea.

Ahoy
there!

Bob...bob...bob...

12

Bob...bob...bob...

Bob...bob...bob...bob...

Lots of animals' heads...

MeOw!

Woof woof!

Oink!

MOO!

15

1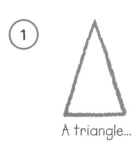
A triangle...

2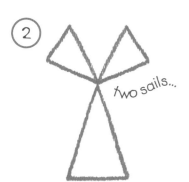
two sails...

3
two more...

4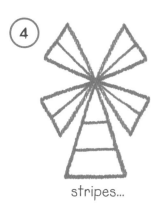
stripes...

5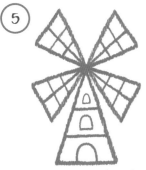
...windows and a door.

Draw windmills and tulips.

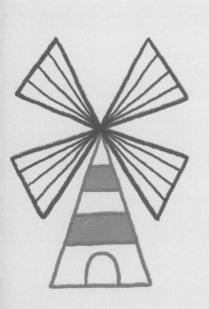

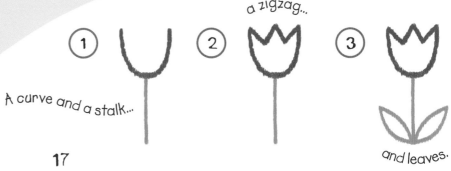

A curve and a stalk...

a zigzag...

① ② ③

and leaves.

...and fill in our feathers.

19

Doodle swirls and curls...

...and dots and spots.

Draw around the edges.

Draw spots or dots?

22

Add stripes?

23

Draw dragons in Dragonland.

Whoosh!

1 A head and a body...

2 lines for a neck and wings...

3 a tail... and finish the wings.

(4) Add four legs...

(5) ears and a triangle on the tail...

(6) eyes, nostrils and spikes.

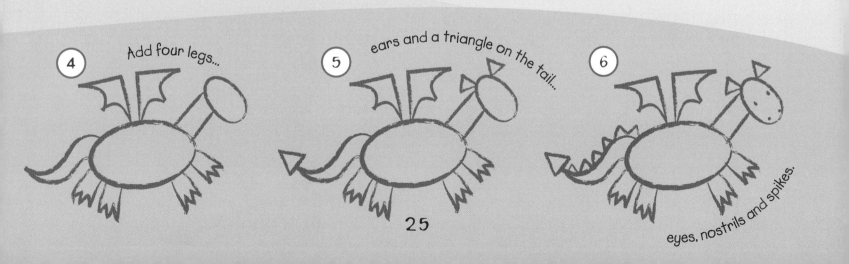

These giraffes need some spots.
Can you help them?

I'd like orange spots!

I like pink
and purple.

① A rectangle and a triangle...

② two small rectangles...

③ four little triangles...

④ and flames.

Draw rockets and planets in space.

Ideas for different planets

Whoooooooosh!

28

Add curls, lines and zigzag fur, and looping lines on the acorns.

How many balls can the seals balance on their noses?

Draw knights in a castle.

Halt!

① A rectangle...

② a shield...

③ a helmet...

④ two lines...

32

5 a face...

and feet...

6 two arms...

7 a sword...

8 eyes, nose and mouth.

33

Fill the white shapes with lots of bright patterns.

35

These racing cars should be nice and bright...

Vroo0000oom!

I'll be last if I don't hurry.

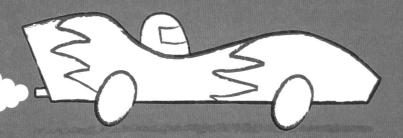

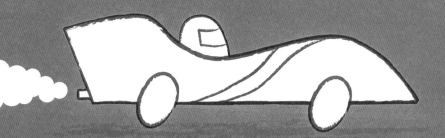

I'm catching up.

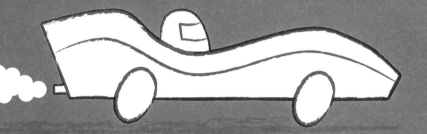

I'm winning!

Vroo0OOOoom!

Draw dolphins diving in the sea.

Splish!

① Draw a body...

② a nose...

③ an eye and mouth.

38

Draw a fatter shape for a whale.

Sploosh!

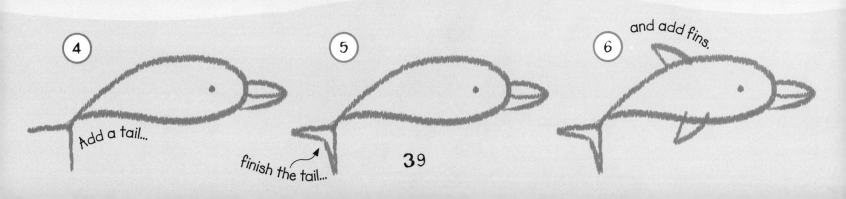

④ Add a tail...

⑤ finish the tail...

39

⑥ and add fins.

This dog could have long, loopy fur.

This Dalmatian needs more spots.

This poodle loves her curly-wurly fur.

WOOF! WOOF!

This dog might like more patches.

Turn each circle into a sun with a happy face.

Doodle raindrops, snowflakes and flashes of lightning.

This gecko likes to show off.

Make him really bright.

This gecko is shy.

If he's green, he'll be able to hide.

44

Please can you fill us in, too?

1

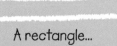

A rectangle...

2

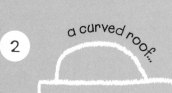

a curved roof...

3

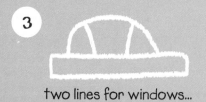

two lines for windows...

4

two wheels...

5

and a curly line.

Draw trucks, cars and houses.

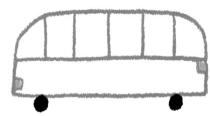

46

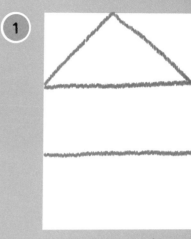

A triangle and a line...

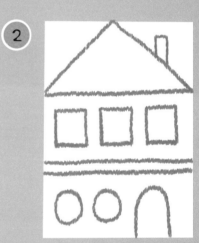

a chimney, windows
and a door...

some smoke...

roof tiles and window panes.

Doodle delicate patterns on the elephants.

Sploosh

Our shells need some lines and spots...

...and we need lots of spikes.

Choose some eyes...

eyebrows?

glasses?

surprised eyes?

eyelashes?

Draw lots of faces.

54

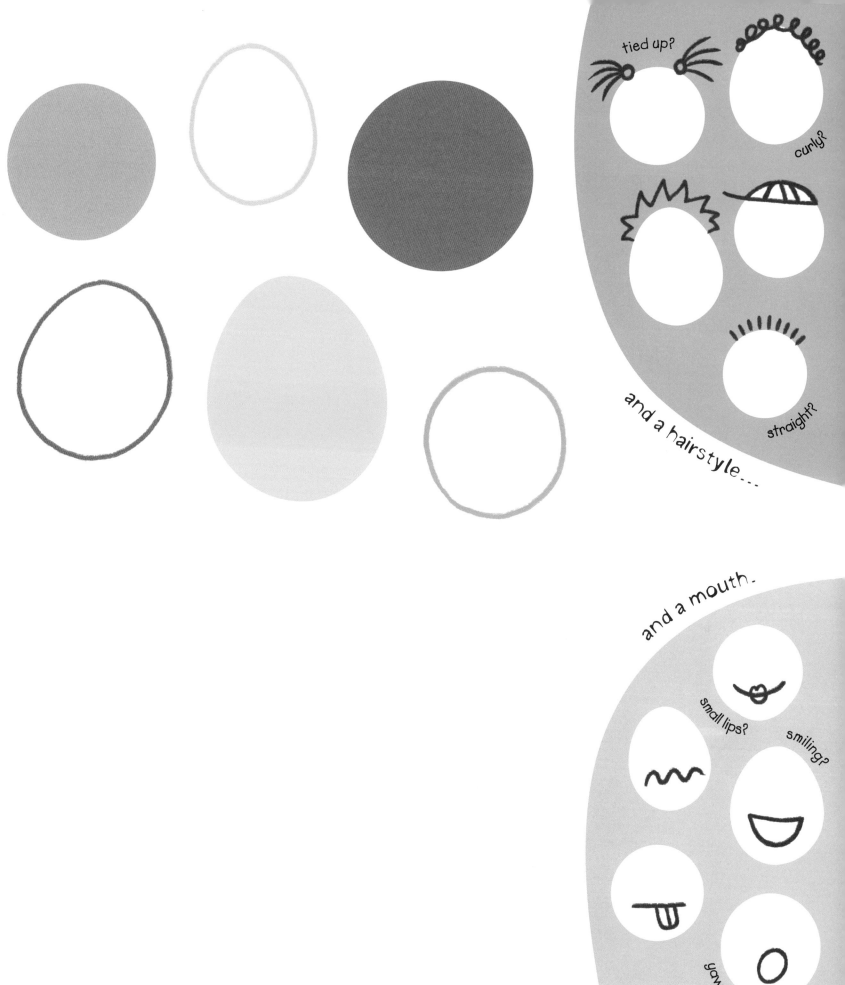

tied up?

curly?

straight?

and a hairstyle...

and a mouth.

small lips?

smiling?

yawning or singing?

55

Tweet

Oh dear! The **patterns** on these clothes have been washed off. Please help.

Fill the spaces with more wet clothes.

Draw ships sailing on the sea.

1 A line and a curve...

2 the front and the back...

3 two sails...

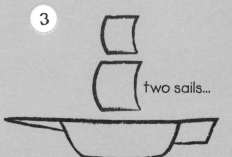

4 two more sails...

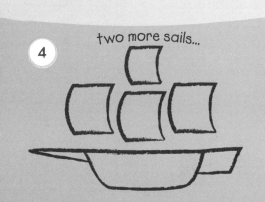

5 lines for the masts...

6 ...and add flags.

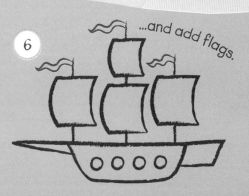

These zebras need some stripes.

Do my stripes have to be black?

60

Draw climbing koalas...

An oval body...

(1)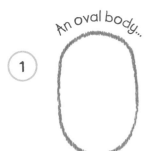

ears...

(2)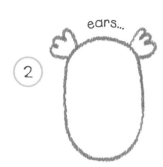

(3)

an arm and paw...

(4)

a leg and foot...

(5)

eyes and a nose.

zzzzzzzzz

...and pandas.

This lonely panda wants some friends.

Round ears...

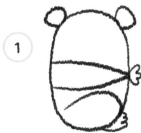

(1)

panda eyes...

(2)

...black and white.

(3)

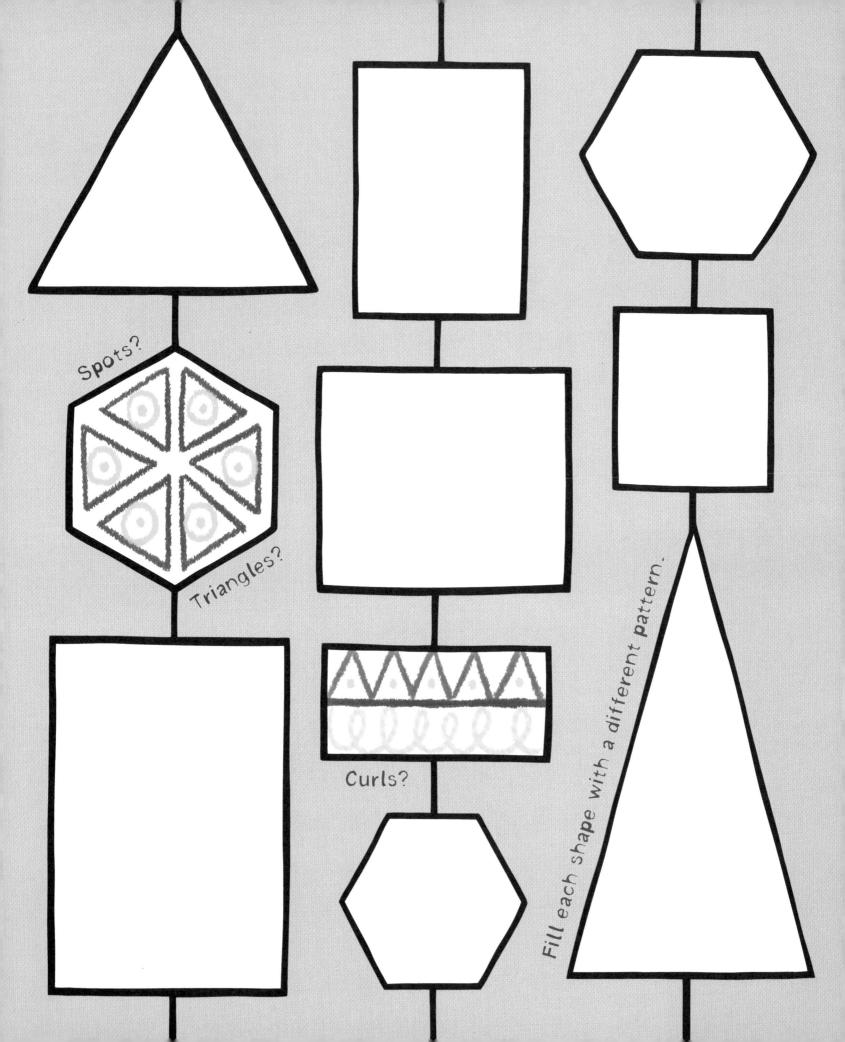

Spots?

Triangles?

Curls?

Fill each shape with a different pattern.

Loops?

Dots?

Purple?

Green?

Red?

1 A head and body...

2 a tail...

3 arms and a line...

4 the end of the tail.

round hands...

Draw mermaids on rocks or swimming in the pool.

68

5 Add hair...

6 a face... and wavy scales.

Sploooooosh!

69

These crocodiles could be green... or orange?

Doodle faces on the **people** on the train.

Add some coal to the empty wagon.

72

Add more faces in the empty windows.

Toot..toot

Some fish are as bright as bright can be...

Blub!

74

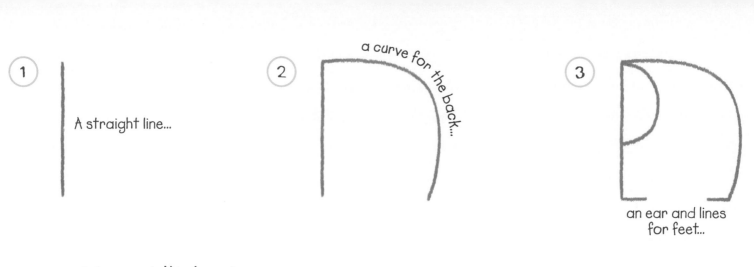

1. A straight line...

2. a curve for the back...

3. an ear and lines for feet...

Draw big and little elephants.

Splooooosh!

(4)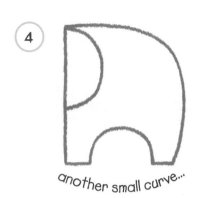

another small curve...

(5)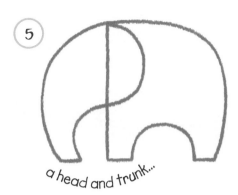

a head and trunk...

(6)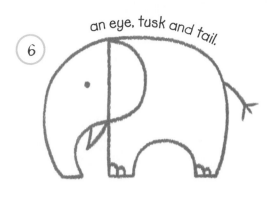

an eye, tusk and tail.

Please decorate my blanket.

77

Doodle wavy feathers and wings...

78

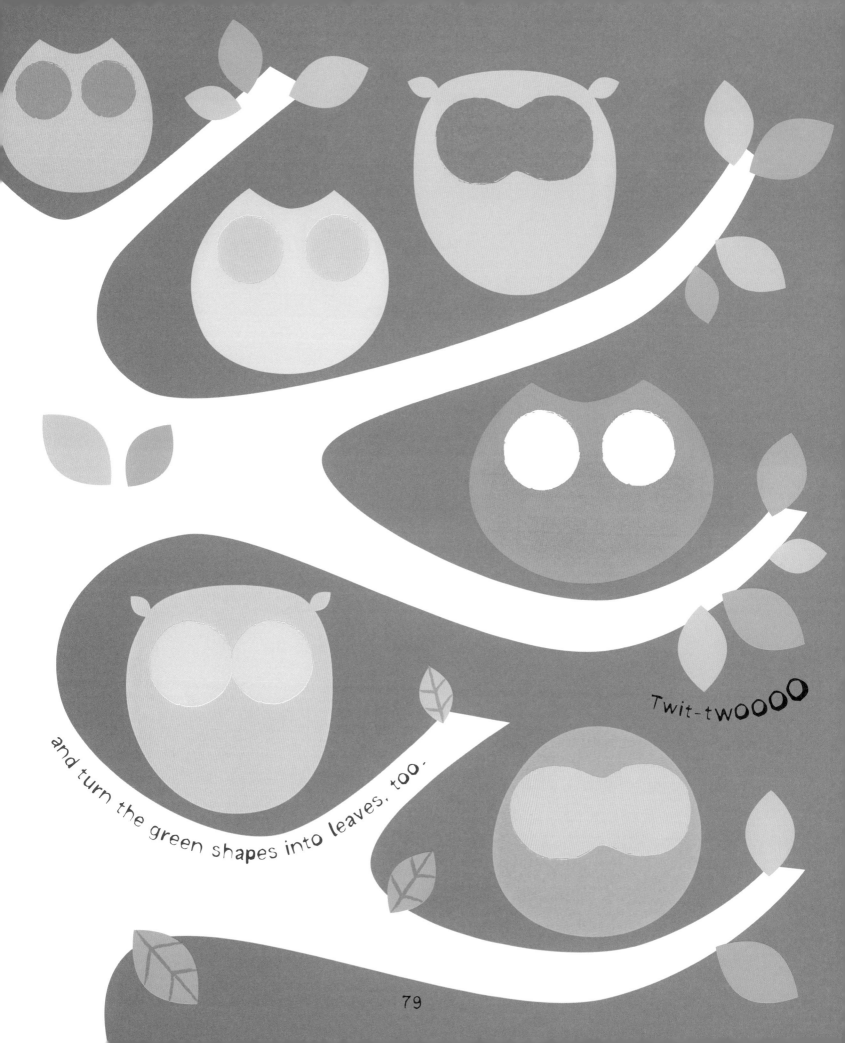

and turn the green shapes into leaves, too.

Twit-twOOOO

Fresh green apples...

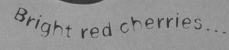

Bright red cherries...

Pink strawberries...

and green pears...

Turn these white shapes into snowmen.

I'm freeeeezing!

I'm cold, too!

82

83

Snuffle

Draw hedgehogs and toadstools.

① A curved top...

② a fat stalk...

③ and lots of spots.

1

A head and body...

2

an eye, nose and mouth...

3

lots of spikes and feet.

I love blue.

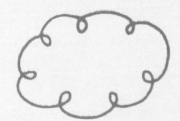

Draw planes in the sky...

Draw these shapes...

two wings...

tail fins...

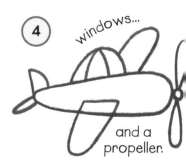

windows...

and a propeller.

WhoooOOOosh!

...add some helicopters, too.

Chugga...chugga

1 Draw an oval...

2 landing gear...

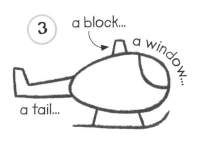

3 a tail...
a block...
a window...

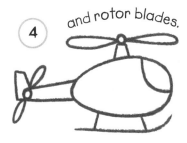

4 and rotor blades.

Turn the brown shapes into monkeys ...

Oo...oo..ee..ee

...and doodle more leaves on the tree, too.

91

Draw cats on walls.

1 A head and body...

2 four legs...

3 a tail and two ears...

4 a face and some whiskers.

1 A head and body...

2 front legs...

93

3 a tail and two ears...

4 a face and some whiskers.

Fill the empty shapes with different patterns.

Bright shells...

Spiral shells...

Spots...

...and stripes.

97

I have spots...

I have stripes...

...and I need some more legs.

Turn the shapes into bugs.

Doodle lots of little legs...

...and add spots, stripes and swirls.

Draw diggers on the building site.

① Draw two rectangles...

② the tracks...

③ a window and wheels...

④ a radiator, handle and spots in the wheels.

100

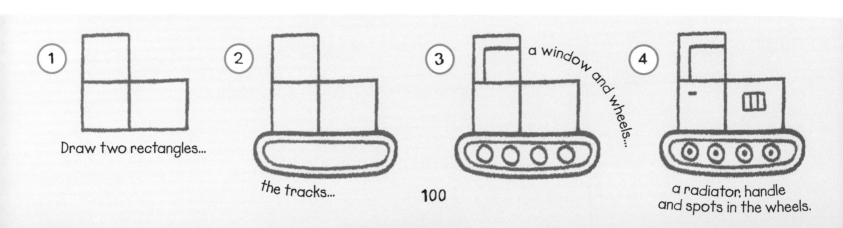

Chug...chug!

Draw more rocks to be lifted.

Tools to attach

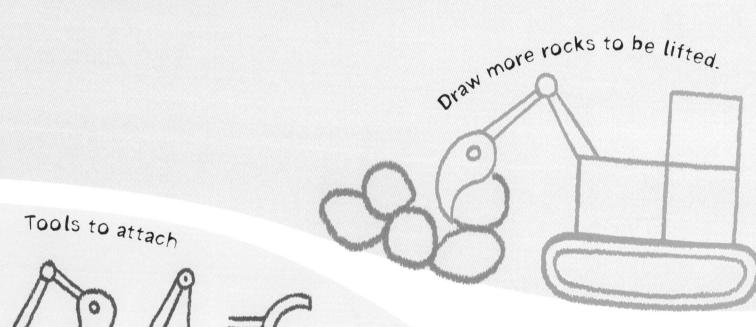

an excavator

a lifter

a grabber

101

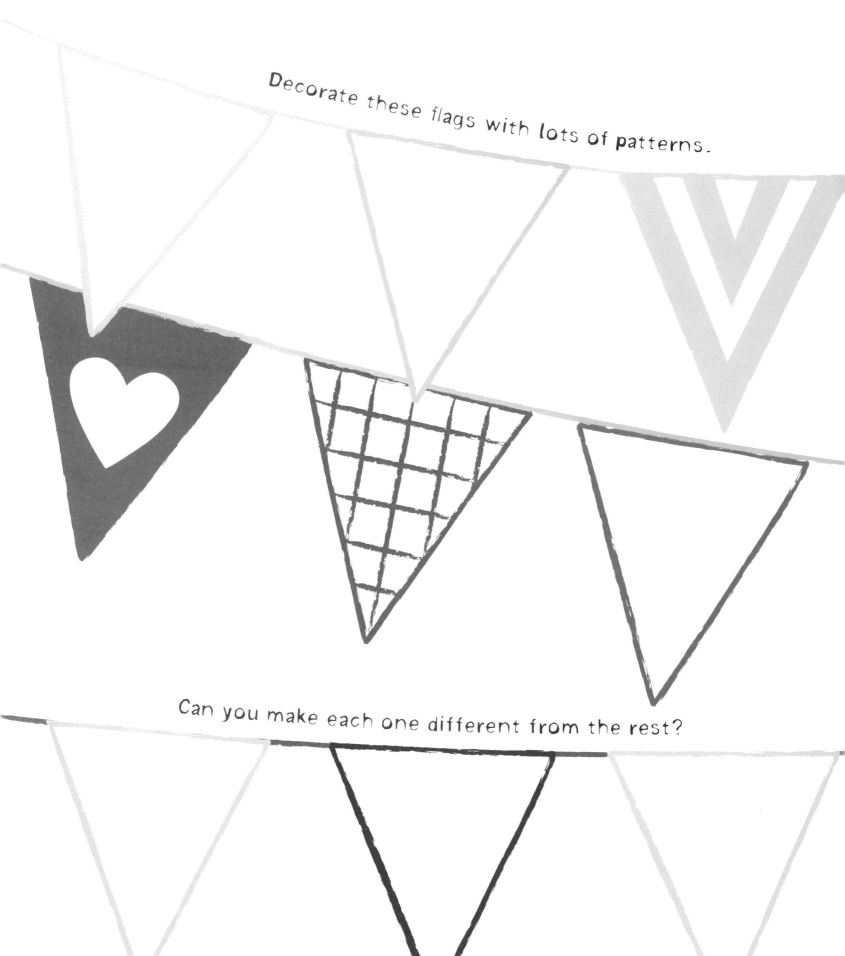

Decorate these flags with lots of patterns.

Can you make each one different from the rest?

Add spiky teeth and fins to these hungry sharks.

Snap!

Fill in the lines...

...and the spots.

1 Two lines like this...

2 a curved tummy...

3 a head...

Draw birds on the branches.

Squawk!

④ a beak and an eye...

⑤ a wing and claws...

⑥ and a long tail.

Screech!

You could fill these shapes...

...or add more patterns.

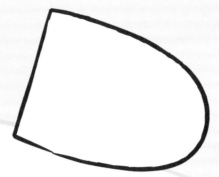

Turn the shapes into penguins having fun in the snow.

Doodle some hats to keep them warm.

Wheeeeeeee!

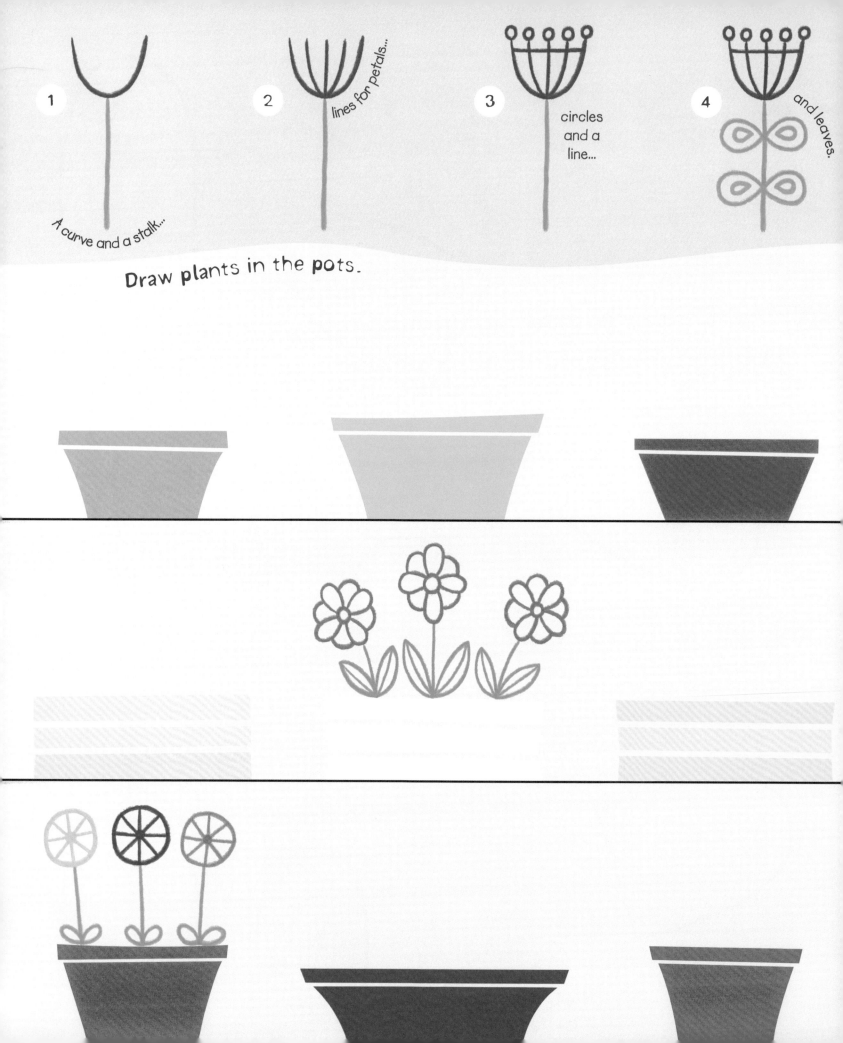

1 A curve and a stalk...

2 lines for petals...

3 circles and a line...

4 and leaves.

Draw plants in the pots.

1 A circle...

2 lots of petals...

3 dots and a stalk...

4 two leaves.

Add patterns to the planets.

zonk-zonk.

Hello down there!

Brighten
the stars.

117

Where are the bunnies' ears and tails?

Give them lots of carrots, too.

119

① A head...

② a long body and tail...

③ a wavy line...

Draw lizards crawling along branches.

Slurp!

120

④ bent legs...

⑤ and toes.

Hello, my name is Lara.

We'd like to be bright and pretty...

I'm Natasha.

I'm Rosa.

Can you think of names
for the rest of us?

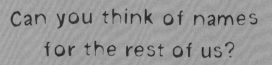

1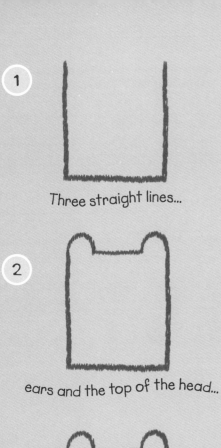

Three straight lines...

2

ears and the top of the head...

3

a line...

and four paws...

4

eyes, a nose and a mouth...

5

a tie and some stripes.

It's cold!

Draw bears in the woods.

125

Doodle a face and eight legs on each spider.

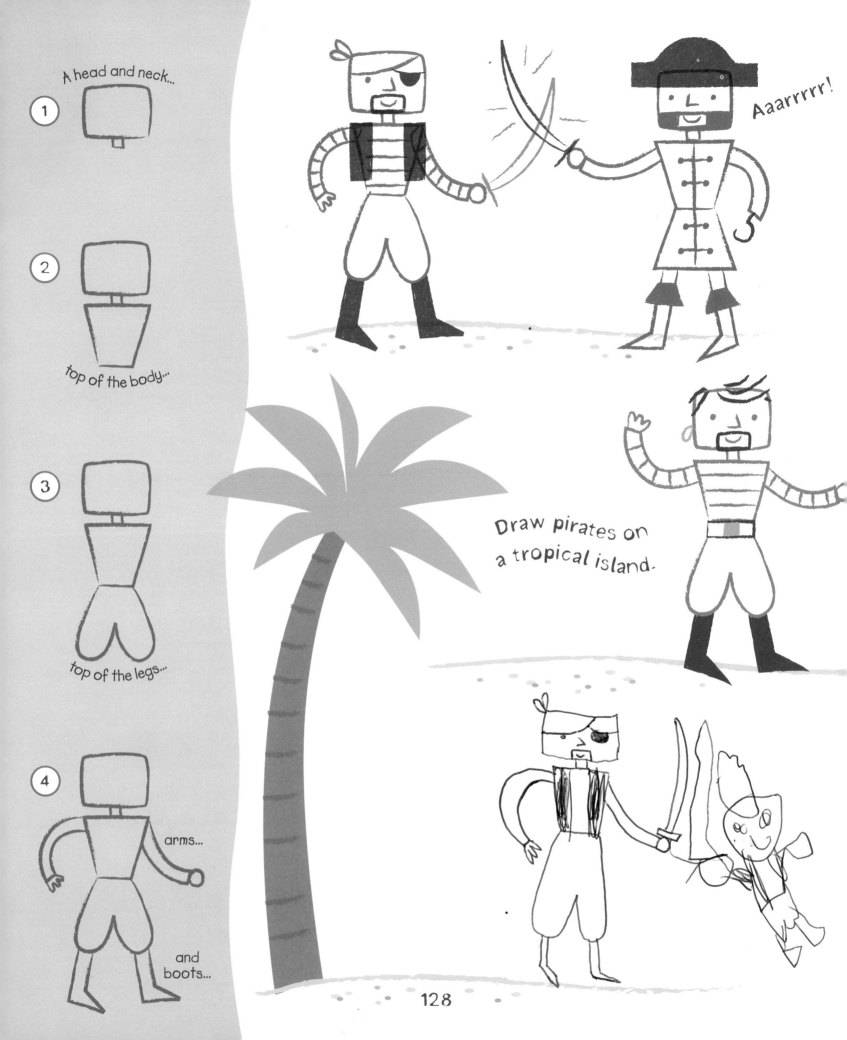

A head and neck...

①

② top of the body...

③ top of the legs...

④ arms...

and boots...

Aaarrrrr!

Draw pirates on a tropical island.

128

a headscarf...

5

a face and eyepatch...

6

and a jacket and cutlass.

7

Yo ho ho!

129

Doodle on these circles to turn them into faces...

Sleepy

Ooooo!

Yo-ho-ho!

Don't cry...

...and add some more faces to fill the empty spaces.

131

Can you brighten this garden?

Pretty flowers...

Beautiful butterflies...

---and busy bees.

133

Doodle on the flags and towers...

...and draw lots more flags and another tower, too.

Draw buzzing bees and fluttering butterflies.

1 A body...

2 wings...

3 an eye and stripes.

Buzzzzzz

A body...

1

four wings...

2

and feelers.

3

Let's go fly a kite...

Up...up...and away!

Make these kites
look bright.

139

Draw dragonflies and flowers.

1 A body...

2 four wings...

3 eyes and stripes.

Bzzzzzzzzzz

1 Flower petals...

2 lines and dots.

141

You could do squiggly lines to fill this tree with bushy leaves.

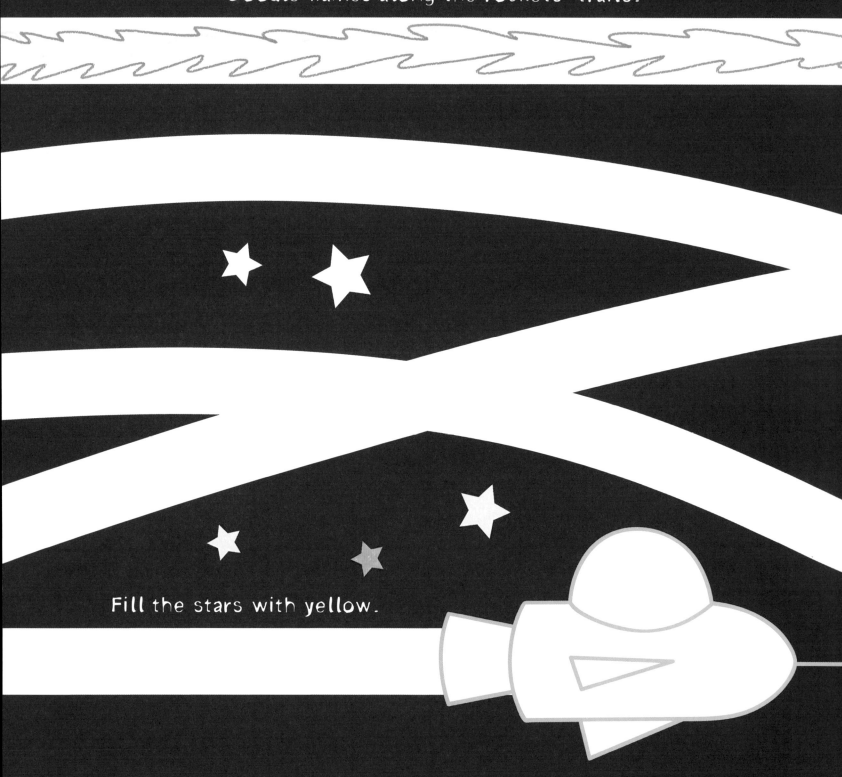

Doodle flames along the rockets' trails.

Fill the stars with yellow.

Doodle lines and bolts on the rockets....

... and add spacemen.

ZooOOOoom!

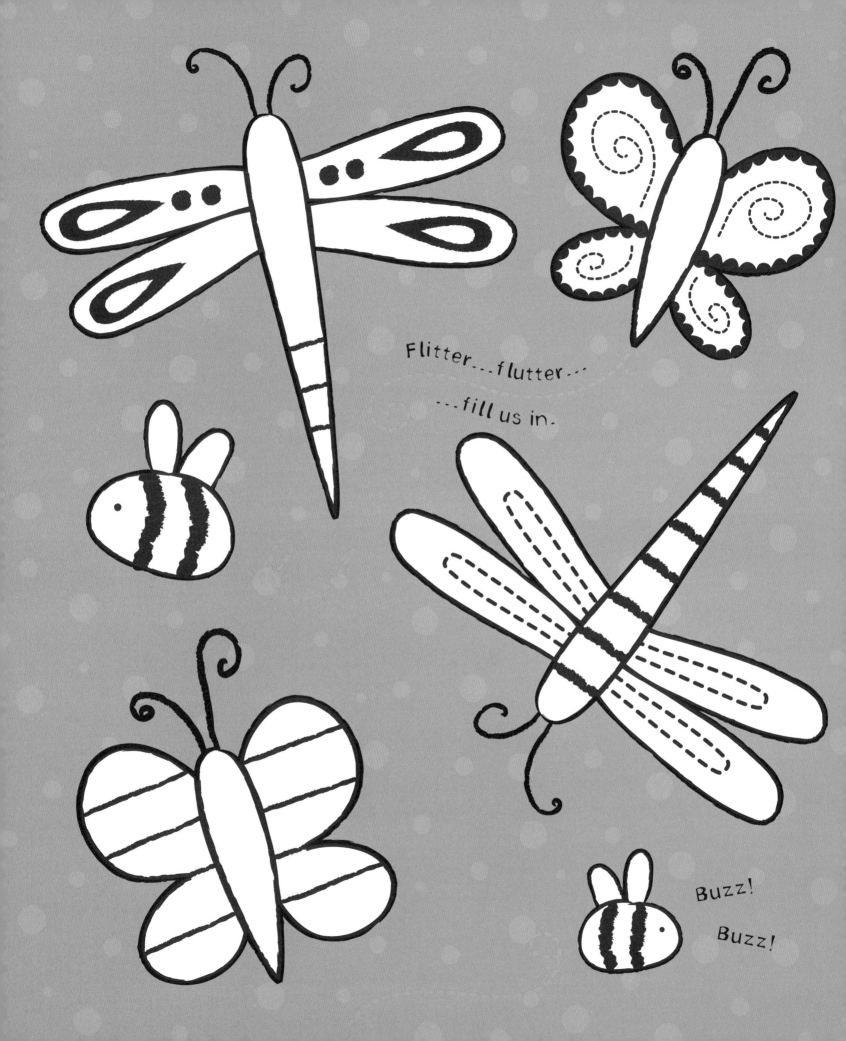

Flitter...flutter...

...fill us in.

Buzz!

Buzz!

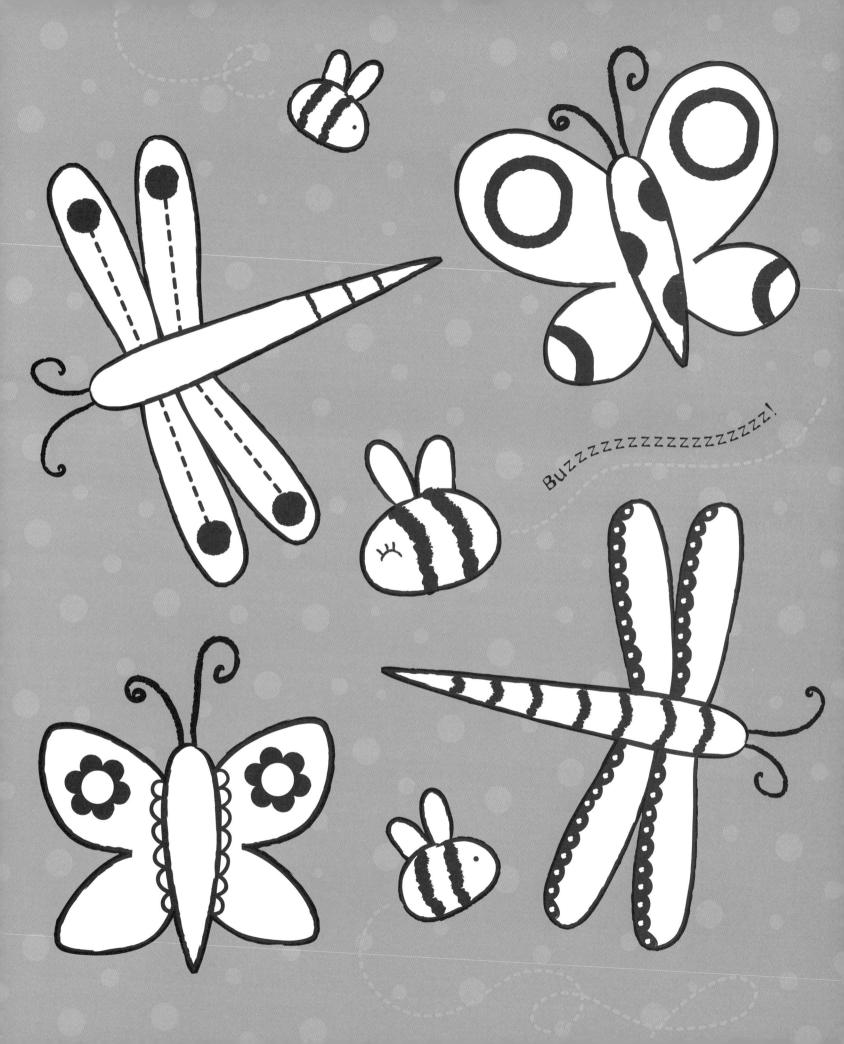

Buzzzzzzzzzzzzzzzzz!

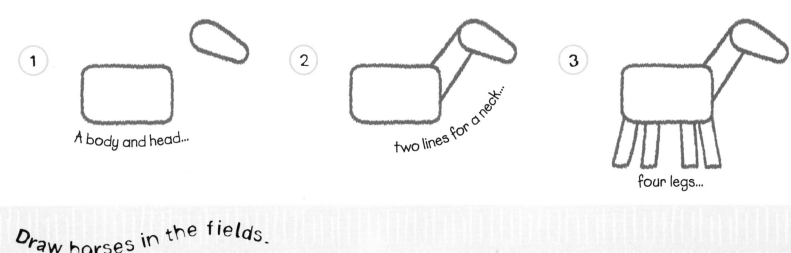

1. A body and head...

2. two lines for a neck...

3. four legs...

Draw horses in the fields.

Neigh!

4 ears and an eye... a nose and mouth... hooves...

5 a mane and a tail...

6 spots on the body... and fill in the hooves.

Chomp...chomp...

149

These houses need windows and doors...

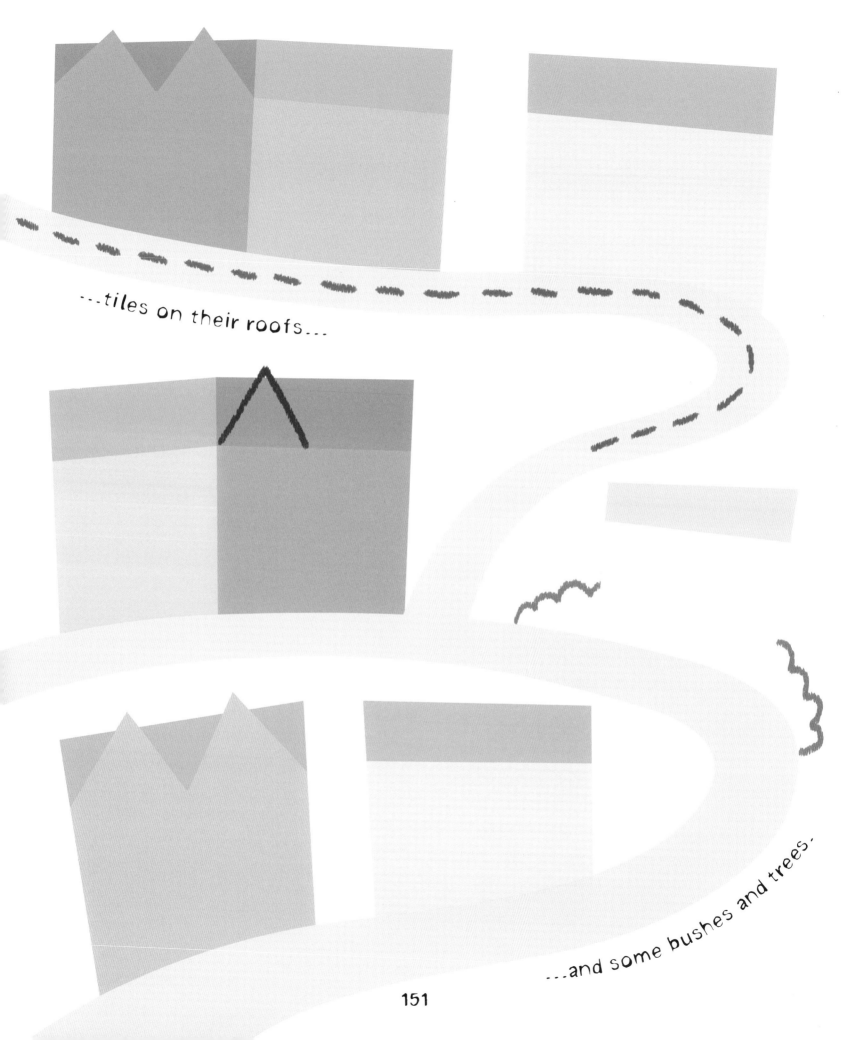

...tiles on their roofs...

...and some bushes and trees.

1 A head with ears...

2 a curly mane...

3 a body...

Draw lions hiding the grass.

I'm a lioness.
I don't have a mane.

④ four legs...

⑤ eyes and a nose...

⑥ and a tail.

ZZZZZZZ

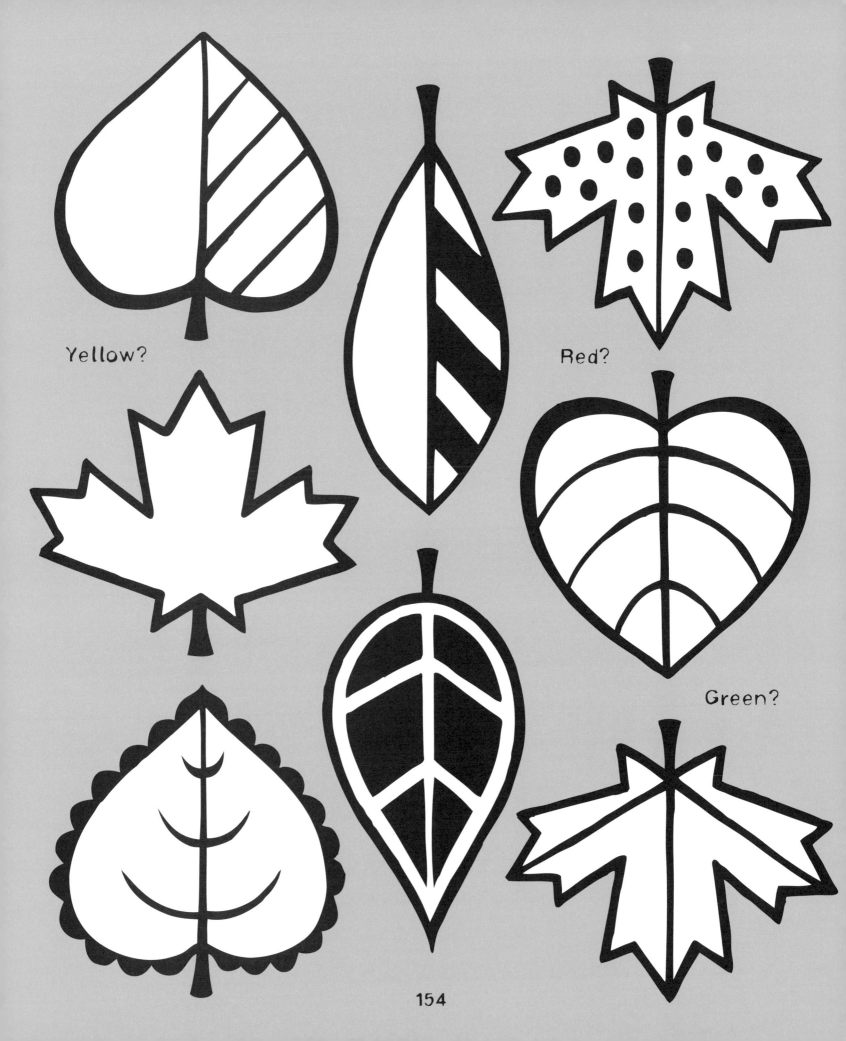

Yellow?

Red?

Green?

154

Orange?

Brown?

Doodle patterns on the monster trucks.

Add some dust or smoke.

VrooOOOoom!

VrooOoom!

157

Splash!

Splooosh!

These elephants could be blue, or red... or pink?

Please fill in my shell!

Follow the trails with a crayon to catch **up** with these snails.

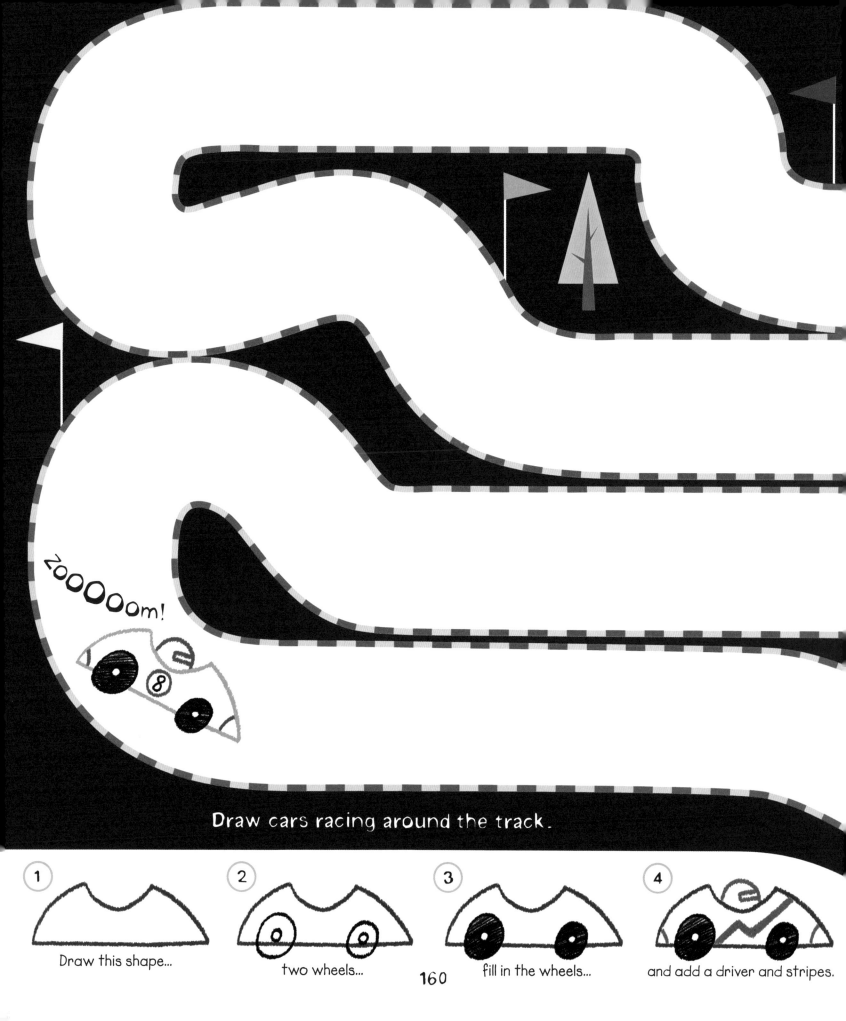

zoOOOom!

Draw cars racing around the track.

1 Draw this shape...

2 two wheels...

3 fill in the wheels...

4 and add a driver and stripes.

160

Be careful at the corner.

vroOOOom!

The finish line!

We need some scales to help us swim.

162

splish...

splash...

splosh!

163

Fresh greens...

Bright reds...

Cool blues....

Sunny yellows....

Can you fill these empty shapes?

166

Then fill this empty space with shapes of your own.

Croak!

Draw frogs on lily pads.

A body...

① ② big eyes...

③ four legs...

feet and spots.

④

Croak!

Croak!

Baa!

Doodle lots of curly wool on the sheep...

170

...and draw wavy patterns on the goats.

Baa!

171

If these shapes are filled in with cool blues and purples they will look like ice-cold snowflakes.

172

If they are filled in with warm yellows, oranges and reds, they will look like fiery stars.

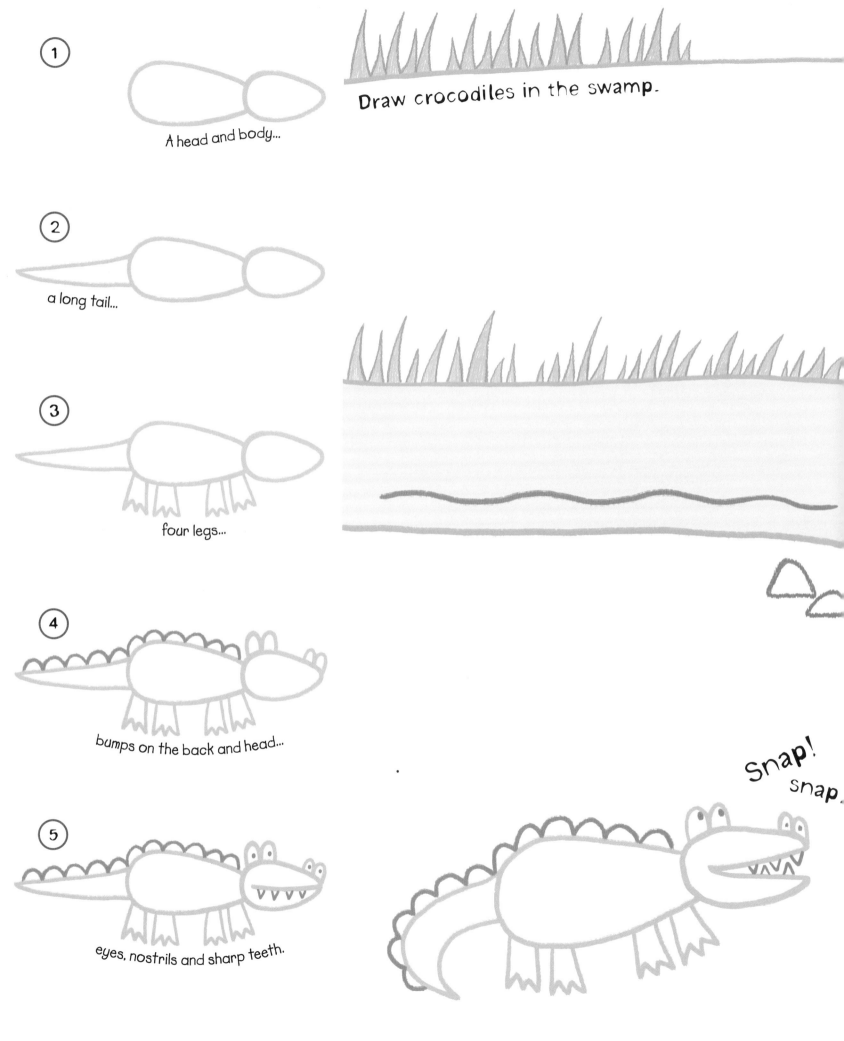

1. A head and body...

2. a long tail...

3. four legs...

4. bumps on the back and head...

5. eyes, nostrils and sharp teeth.

Draw crocodiles in the swamp.

Snap!
Snap.

Fill in these
shapes.

176

Make them as different as you can.

177

1

A head and triangle
for a dress...

2

four wings...

3

arms and legs...

Draw fairies flying around the flowers.

I'd like a wand.

add hair...
4

hands and feet...
5

eyes and a smile.
6

Turn these blobs into monsters.

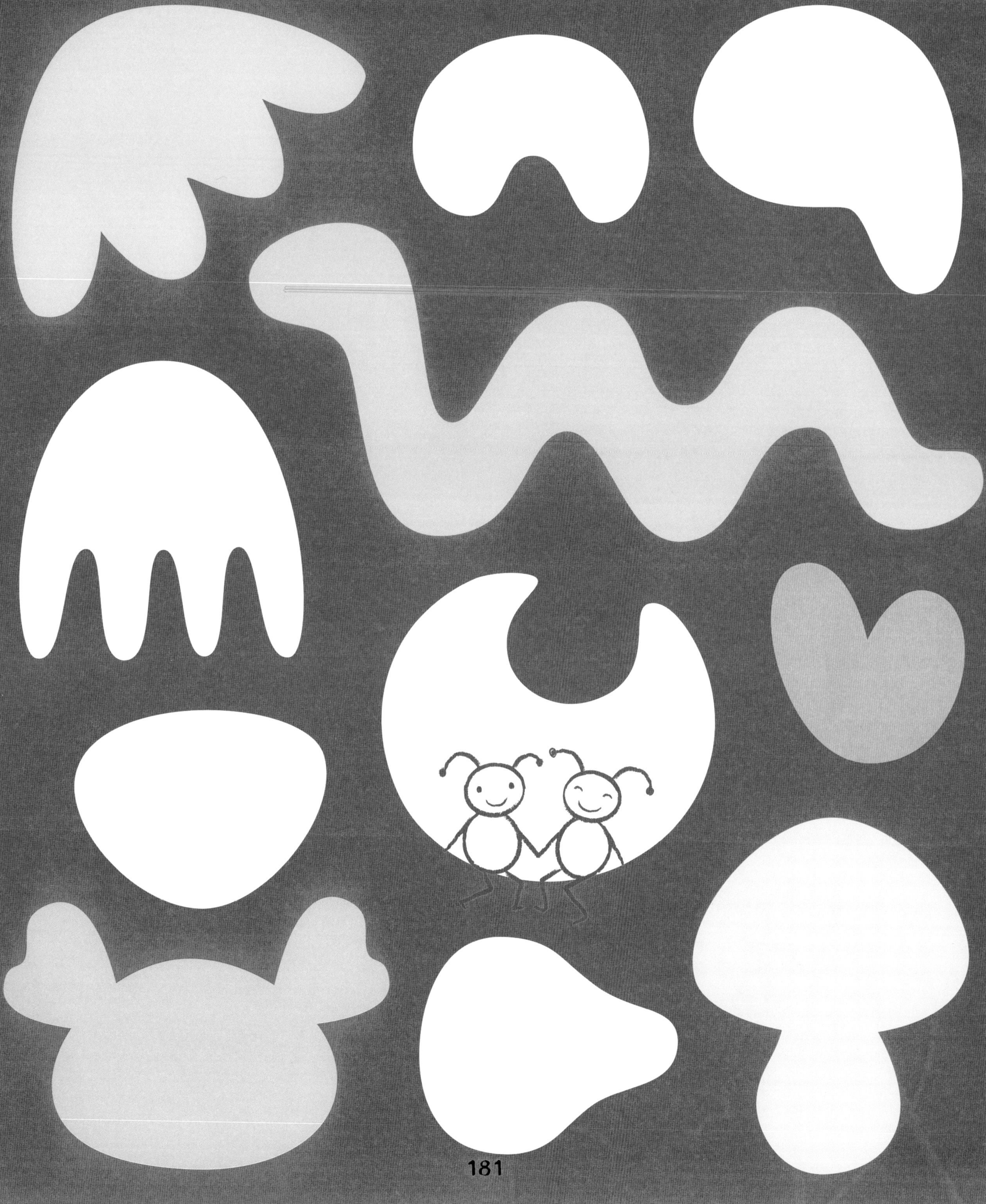

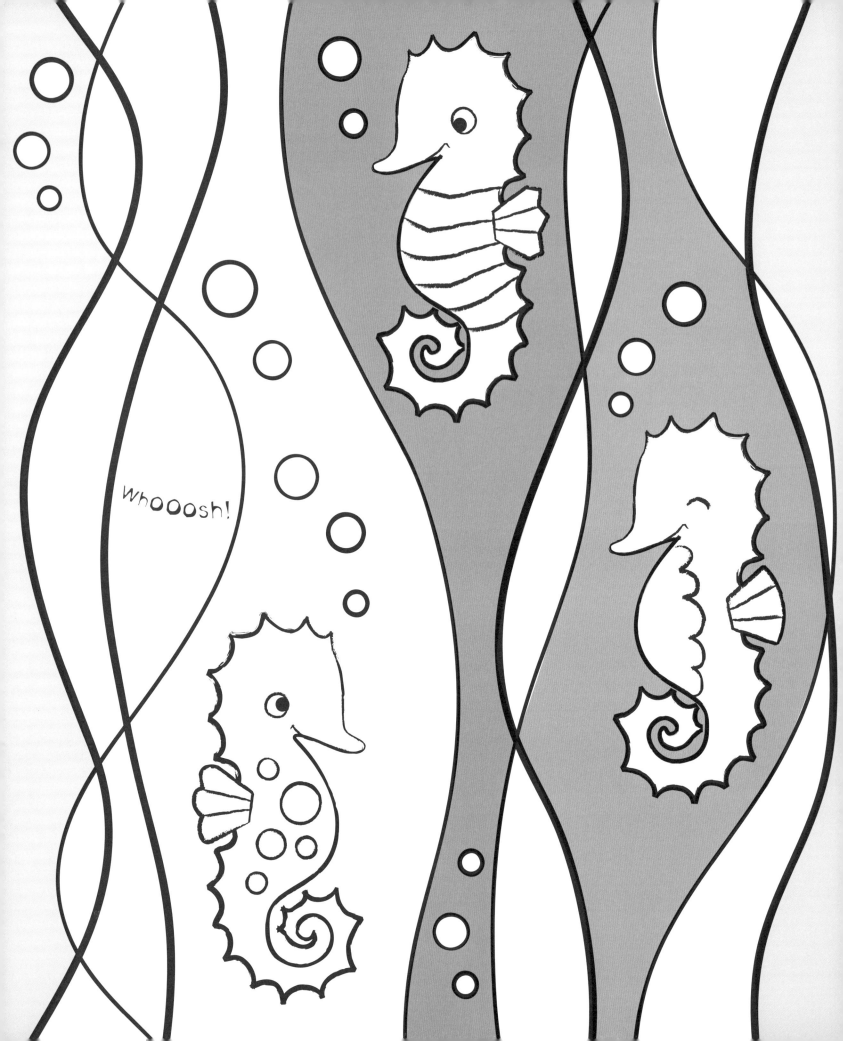

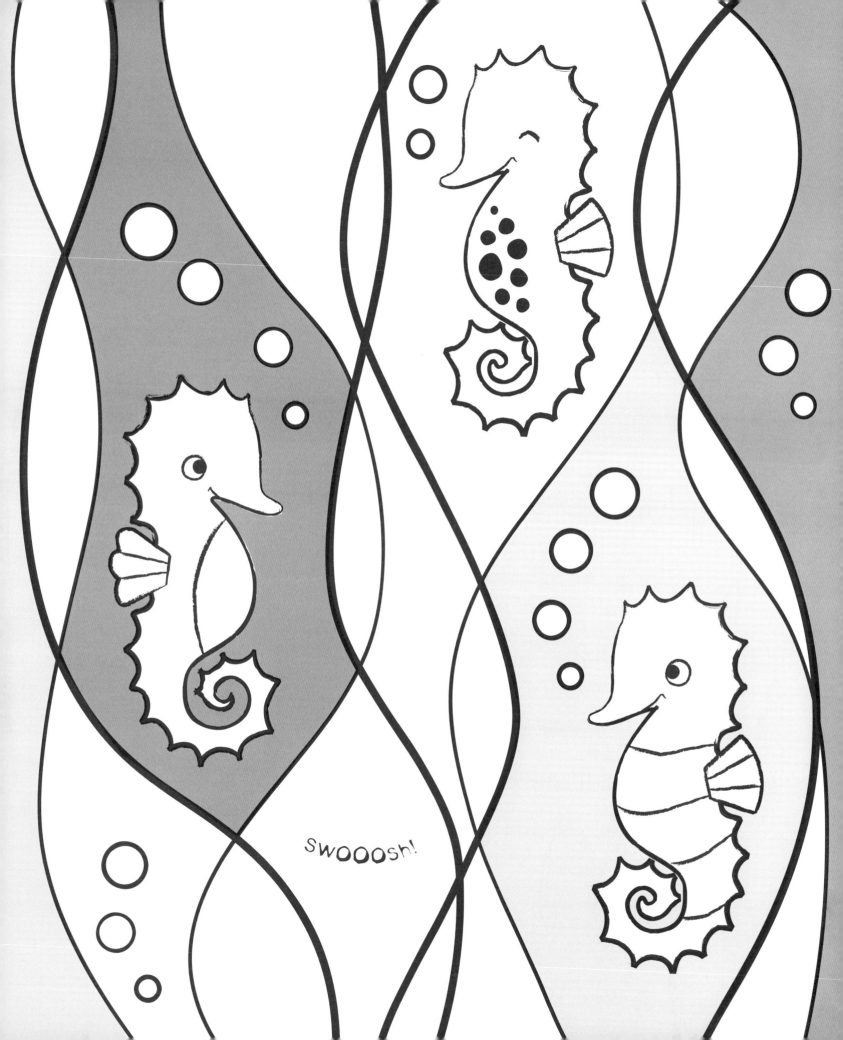

swooosh!

1 An oval body...

2 a small head...

3 lines for a neck...

Draw hungry dinosaurs.

Chomp! chomp!

(4) four stumpy legs...

(5) a long tail...

(6) and lots of spikes.

Doodle lots of bright spots on the toadstools.

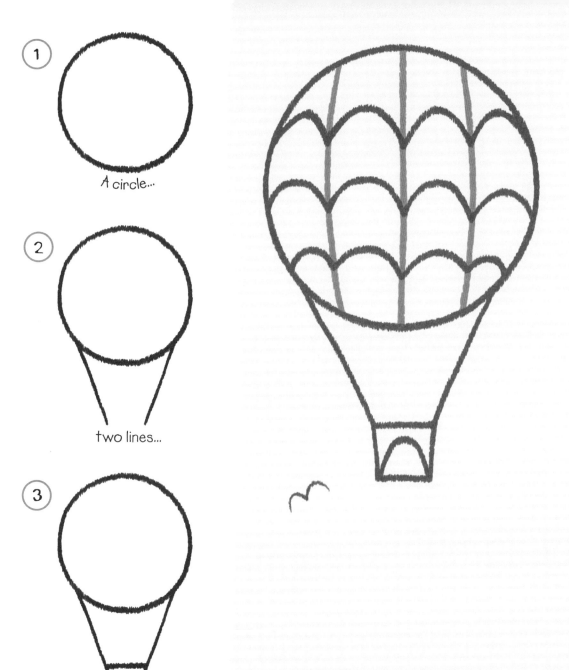

1. A circle...

2. two lines...

3. a basket...

4.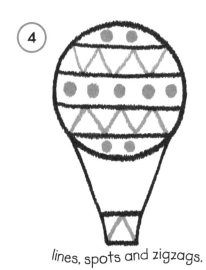
lines, spots and zigzags.

Draw hot-air balloons floating across the sky.

Turn this circle into a balloon.

We'd love to have some eyes, wings and feathery patterns.

191

1. A head and body...

2. four legs...

3. a tail... ears and a face.

Woof!

Draw dogs chasing a ball, birds and a cat.

Squawk!

Meow!

First published in 2013 by Usborne Publishing Ltd., 83-85 Saffron Hill, London, EC1N 8RT, England www.usborne.com
Copyright © 2013, 2012, 2011 Usborne Publishing Ltd. The name Usborne and the devices ♀⊕ are Trade Marks of Usborne Publishing Ltd.
All rights reserved. No part of this publication may be reproduced, stored in a retrieval system, or transmitted in any form or by any means,
electronic, mechanical, photocopy, recording or otherwise, without prior permission of the publisher. UE First published in America 2013.
Printed in Dongguan, Guangdong, China.